FOREWORD

Happiness and Boys and Girls — they seem to go hand in hand; especially in singing. It is not only a happy time for the singers, but also for those who are privileged to listen.

In HAPPYTIME BOOK TWO, you will find a wealth of songs written and arranged with boys and girls in mind. May they bring happiness to many.

THE PUBLISHERS

I'M AS HAPPY AS I CAN BE

C. M. T.

CORA MAE TAYLOR

I'm free as a bird on the moun-tain! I'm hap-py as I can be! I'm drink-ing to-day at the foun-tain That is flow-ing from Cal-va-ry. Ho! ev-'ry-one that thirst-eth, Come ye to the wa-ters Flow-ing from sins to set you free! I'm free as a bird on the moun-tain! I'm hap-py as I can be!

Motions: ① Wave hands. ② Clap hands. ③ Imitate drinking from a cup. ④ Imitate flowing with hands high and lowering. ⑤ Arms extended in invitation. ⑥ Motion with arms to come.

HAPPY HEARTS

LANTA WILSON

C. A. FYKE

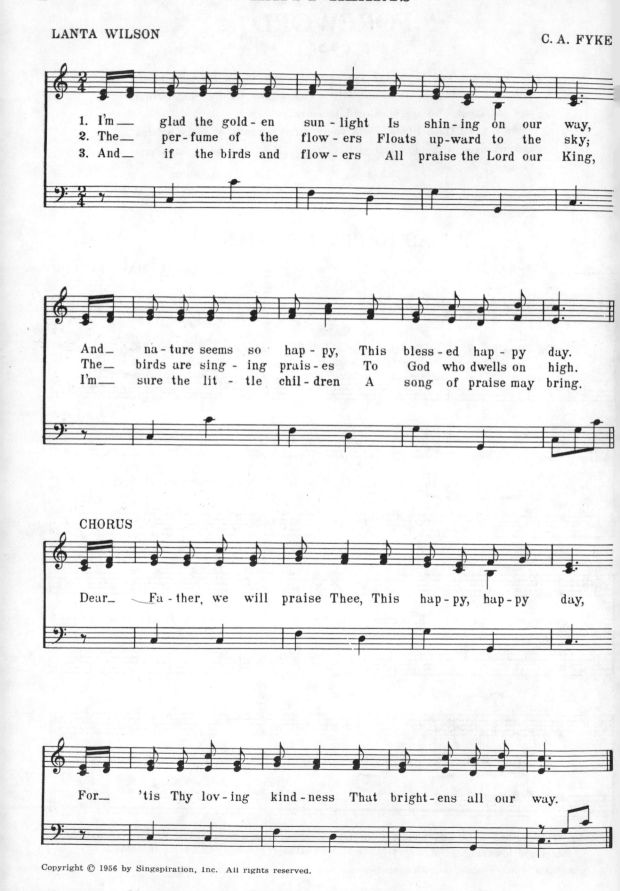

1. I'm __ glad the gold-en sun-light Is shin-ing on our way,
2. The __ per-fume of the flow-ers Floats up-ward to the sky;
3. And __ if the birds and flow-ers All praise the Lord our King,

And __ na-ture seems so hap-py, This bless-ed hap-py day.
The __ birds are sing-ing prais-es To God who dwells on high.
I'm __ sure the lit-tle chil-dren A song of praise may bring.

CHORUS

Dear __ Fa-ther, we will praise Thee, This hap-py, hap-py day,

For __ 'tis Thy lov-ing kind-ness That bright-ens all our way.

PETER, JAMES, AND JOHN IN A SAILBOAT

Old Melody Arr.

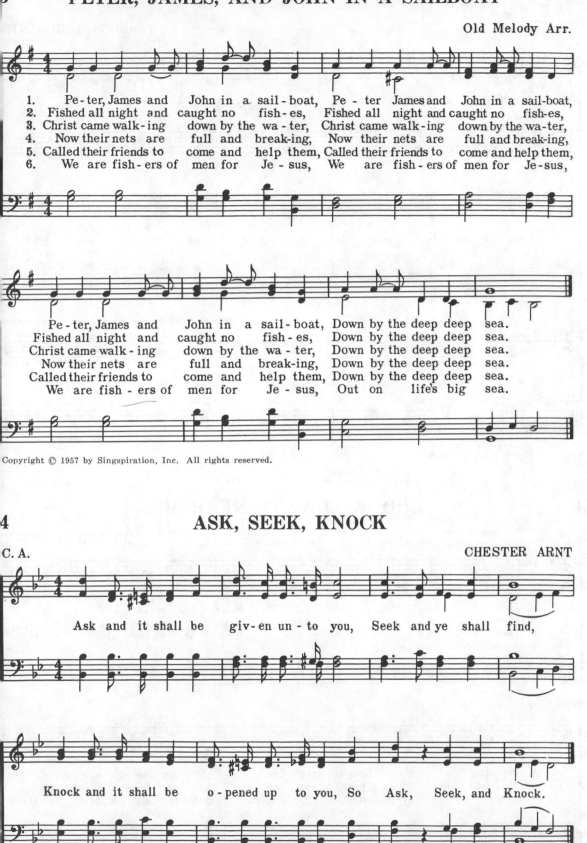

1. Pe-ter, James and John in a sail-boat, Pe-ter James and John in a sail-boat,
2. Fished all night and caught no fish-es, Fished all night and caught no fish-es,
3. Christ came walk-ing down by the wa-ter, Christ came walk-ing down by the wa-ter,
4. Now their nets are full and break-ing, Now their nets are full and break-ing,
5. Called their friends to come and help them, Called their friends to come and help them,
6. We are fish-ers of men for Je-sus, We are fish-ers of men for Je-sus,

Pe-ter, James and John in a sail-boat, Down by the deep deep sea.
Fished all night and caught no fish-es, Down by the deep deep sea.
Christ came walk-ing down by the wa-ter, Down by the deep deep sea.
Now their nets are full and break-ing, Down by the deep deep sea.
Called their friends to come and help them, Down by the deep deep sea.
We are fish-ers of men for Je-sus, Out on life's big sea.

ASK, SEEK, KNOCK

C. A.

CHESTER ARNT

Ask and it shall be giv-en un-to you, Seek and ye shall find,

Knock and it shall be o-pened up to you, So Ask, Seek, and Knock.

THE BIBLE IS PRECIOUS TO ME

F. J. R.

FRANCES J. ROBERTS

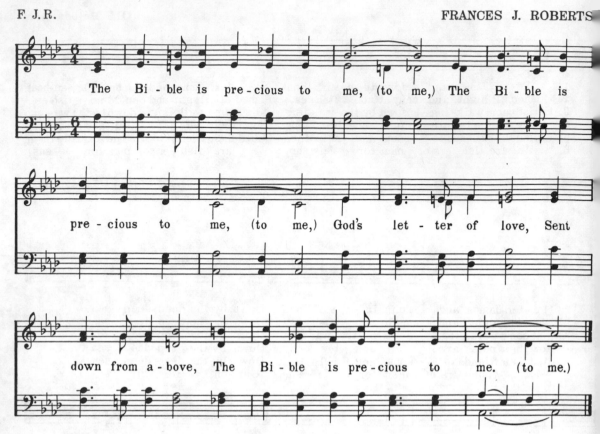

The Bi-ble is pre-cious to me, (to me,) The Bi-ble is pre-cious to me, (to me,) God's let-ter of love, Sent down from a-bove, The Bi-ble is pre-cious to me. (to me.)

6   GOD IS ALWAYS NEAR ME

ALFRED B. SMITH

1. God is al-ways near me, Hear-ing what I say,
2. God is al-ways near me, In the dark-est night,
3. God is al-ways near me, Tho so young and small,

Know-ing all my thoughts and deeds, All my work and play.
He can see me just as well As by morn-ing light.
Not a look or word or thought But God knows it all.

7 SING HOSANNA

Verses: JOHN W. PETERSON

Arr. by The CSEHYS

1. What a won-der-ful Sav-iour is Je-sus,_____ What a won-der-ful friend is He;_____ For He left all the glo-ry of heav-en,_____ Came to earth to die on Cal-va-ry._____

2. He a-rose from the grave, Hal-le-lu-jah!_____ And He lives nev-er-more to die;_____ At the Fa-ther's right hand in-ter-ced-ing_____ He will hear and heed our faint-est cry._____

3. He is com-ing some day to re-ceive us,_____ We'll be caught up to man-sions a-bove_____ What a joy it will be to be-hold Him,_____ Sing for-ev-er of His grace and love!_____

2 PART CHORUS

Sing_____ Sing_____ Sing_____ Sing_____
Sing Ho-san-na, Sing Ho-san-na, Sing Ho-san-na to the King of Kings;

Sing_____ Sing_____ Sing_____ Sing
Sing Ho-san-na, Sing Ho-san-na, Sing Ho-san-na to the King.

SUNDAY'S BEST OF ALL

Adapted by J. W. P.

JOHN W. PETERSON

1. The week is made of sev-en days; The days of hours small;
2. This is the day we meet to sing Of our dear home a-bove;
3. For Je-sus is the children's friend, His love makes all things bright,

All days are made for lov-ing deeds, But Sun-day's best of all.
We pray to God our heav'n-ly King, And talk of Je-sus' love.
And heav'n is all one hap-py day, Where we shall dwell in light.

CHORUS

Sun-day's best of all, Sun-day's best of all; We sing God's

praise On all the days, But Sun-day's best of all.

SHINING JUST LIKE THE STARS

H. H. PIERSON

ALFRED B. SMITH &
JOHN W. PETERSON

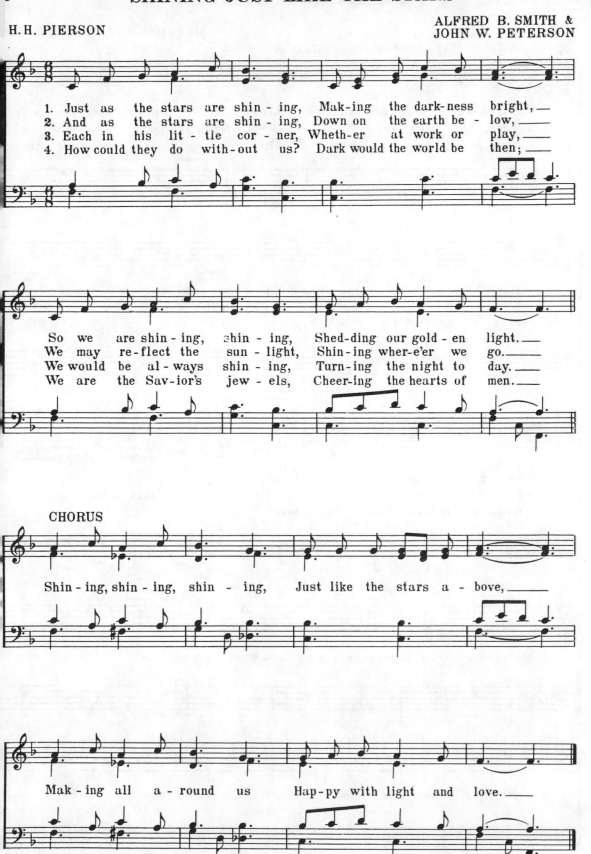

1. Just as the stars are shin-ing, Mak-ing the dark-ness bright,—
2. And as the stars are shin-ing, Down on the earth be-low,—
3. Each in his lit-tle cor-ner, Wheth-er at work or play,—
4. How could they do with-out us? Dark would the world be then;—

So we are shin-ing, shin-ing, Shed-ding our gold-en light.—
We may re-flect the sun-light, Shin-ing wher-e'er we go.—
We would be al-ways shin-ing, Turn-ing the night to day.—
We are the Sav-ior's jew-els, Cheer-ing the hearts of men.—

CHORUS

Shin-ing, shin-ing, shin-ing, Just like the stars a-bove,—

Mak-ing all a-round us Hap-py with light and love.—

HIS BANNER OVER US

H. H. L.

HELEN HOWARTH LEMMEL

With martial spirit- Voices in Unison

1. We are chil-dren of the King, And His prais-es we will sing, As we jour-ney to our home a-bove His ban-ner o-ver us is love!
2. He, the glo-rious Son of God, Hath the way be-fore us trod; O-ver ev-'ry foe we'll con-qu'ror prove His ban-ner o-ver us is love! March-ing!
3. Fear-less in our Lead-er's might, Strong to do and dare the right, We will jour-ney to our home a-bove His ban-ner o-ver us is love!

ff REFRAIN *With vigor*

Marked rhythm

March-ing! With hap-py hearts we on-ward move, No foe we fear, with our Cap-tain near His ban-ner o-ver us is love!

11 ISN'T HE WONDERFUL

S. JONES

Arr. by Homer Hammontree

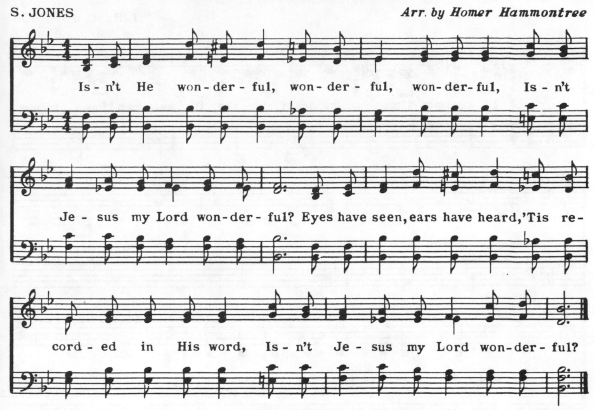

Is-n't He won-der-ful, won-der-ful, won-der-ful, Is-n't
Je-sus my Lord won-der-ful? Eyes have seen, ears have heard, 'Tis re-
cord-ed in His word, Is-n't Je-sus my Lord won-der-ful?

12 TURN YOUR EYES UPON JESUS

H. H. L.

H. H. LEMMEL

Turn your eyes up-on Je-sus Look full in His
won-der-ful face; And the things of earth will grow
strange-ly dim In the light of His glo-ry and grace.

SUMMERTIME IN MY HEART

L. C. J.

LOIS C. JOHNSON

It is sum-mer-time in my heart, Yes, it's sum-mer-time in my
heart; Since Je - sus saved me, New life He gave me,
E - ven in win -ter time it's sum-mer in my heart!
It is sum-mer-time in my heart, Yes, it's sum-mer-time in my
heart; Since Je - sus saved me, New life He gave me,
E - ven in win -ter-time it's sum-mer in my heart!

SUMMERTIME IN MY HEART

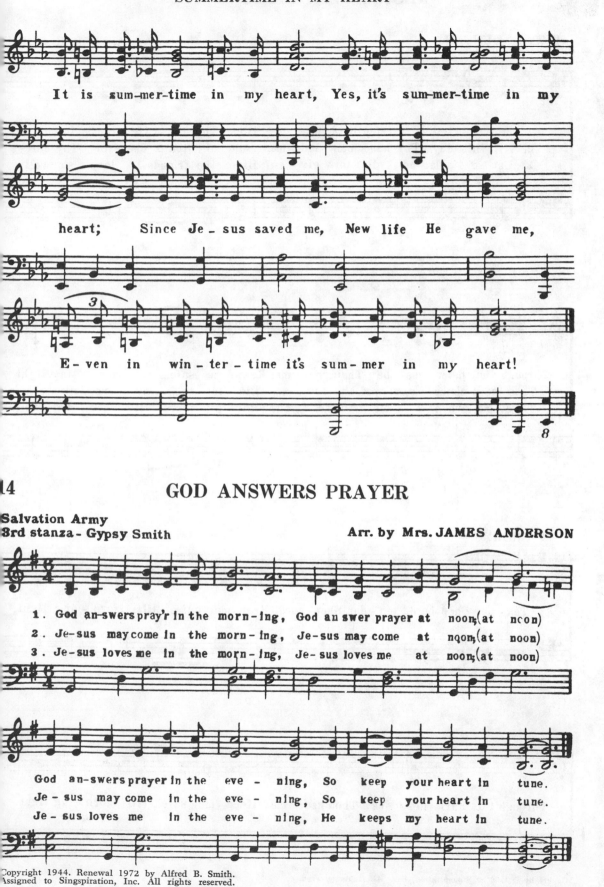

It is sum-mer-time in my heart, Yes, it's sum-mer-time in my heart; Since Je-sus saved me, New life He gave me, E-ven in win-ter-time it's sum-mer in my heart!

GOD ANSWERS PRAYER

Salvation Army
3rd stanza - Gypsy Smith

Arr. by Mrs. JAMES ANDERSON

1. God an-swers pray'r in the morn-ing, God an swer prayer at noon, (at noon)
2. Je-sus may come in the morn-ing, Je-sus may come at noon, (at noon)
3. Je-sus loves me in the morn-ing, Je-sus loves me at noon, (at noon)

God an-swers prayer in the eve-ning, So keep your heart in tune.
Je-sus may come in the eve-ning, So keep your heart in tune.
Je-sus loves me in the eve-ning, He keeps my heart in tune.

JESUS, TENDER SHEPHERD

MERY L. DUNCAN   ALFRED B. SMITH

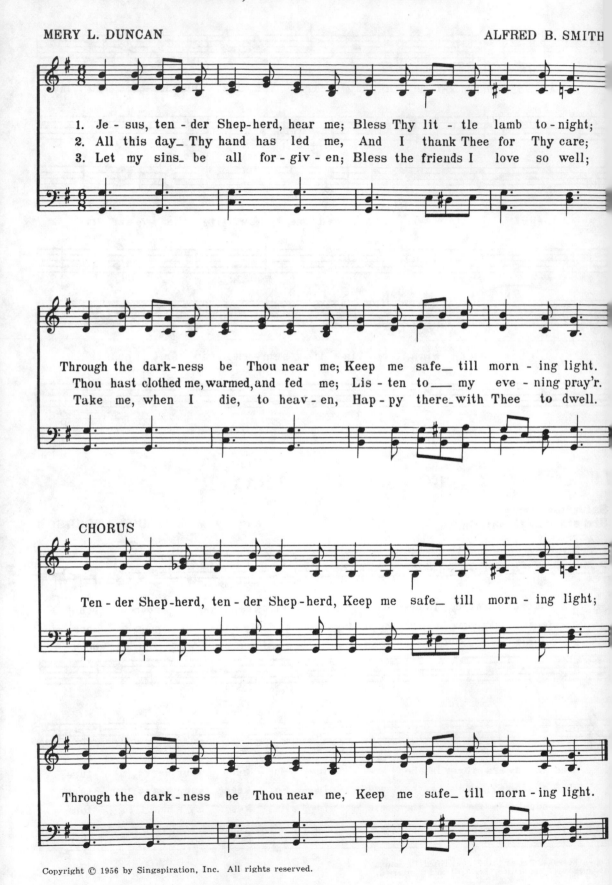

1. Je - sus, ten - der Shep-herd, hear me; Bless Thy lit - tle lamb to-night;
2. All this day_ Thy hand has led me, And I thank Thee for Thy care;
3. Let my sins_ be all for - giv - en; Bless the friends I love so well;

Through the dark-ness be Thou near me; Keep me safe_ till morn - ing light.
Thou hast clothed me, warmed, and fed me; Lis - ten to__ my eve - ning pray'r.
Take me, when I die, to heav - en, Hap - py there_ with Thee to dwell.

CHORUS

Ten - der Shep-herd, ten - der Shep-herd, Keep me safe_ till morn - ing light;

Through the dark-ness be Thou near me, Keep me safe_ till morn - ing light.

GOD LIVES UP THERE

ISABELLA MIDDLEMASS

JOHN W. PETERSON

1. O see the sky, so blue, so high, So ver - y far a - way! Who
2. The day be - gun, who makes the sun Look forth with shin-ing face? When
3. Who lights the star that twink-les far, Just like a lov - ing eye? The

lives up there where all is fair, Dear chil - dren, can you say?
day is done, who takes the sun So quick - ly from its place?
moon so oft, that shin - eth soft, Who draws it through the sky?

CHORUS

God lives up there where all is fair And blue and high and

bright; So great, so kind, none can we find; He keeps us day and night.

GIDEON HAD THE LORD

J.W.P and A.B.S.

JOHN W. PETERSON an
ALFRED B. SMITH

1. Brave Gid-e-on had three hun-dred men, The Mid-i-an-nites had a host;
2. Now if you'd be a sol-dier true, And win a full re-ward;

But Gid-e-on had the Lord with him, And so he had the most.
Be brave and strong in all you do And al-ways trust the Lord.

CHORUS

Gid-e-on had the Lord, Gid-e-on had the Lord; He

won the fight With the Mid-i-an-ites, For Gid-e-on had the Lord.

18 STUDY GOD'S WORD AND HIDE IT IN YOUR HEART

A.B.S.

ALFRED B. SMITH and
JOHN W. PETERSON

Stud-y God's Word and hide it in your heart, Stud-y God's Word and

STUDY GOD'S WORD AND HIDE IT IN YOUR HEART

hide it in your heart; It will keep you ev'ry day, It will

guide you all the way, So stud-y God's Word and hide it in your heart.

19   ## SUNSHINE IN MY HEART

C. M. T.
CORA MAE TAYLOR

What though the skies be dark and gray. Be dark and gray, be dark and gray!

What though the skies be dark and gray, The sun is shin-ing to - day!

The sun is shin-ing, the sun is shin-ing, Though clouds may keep us a - part.

What though the skies be dark and gray, There's sun-shine in my heart.

GRUMBLERS

T. H.

THORO HARRIS

1. In coun-try, town or ci-ty some peo-ple can be found
2. They grum-ble in the ci-ty, they grum-ble on the farm,
3. They grum-ble when it's rain-ing, they grum-ble when it's dry,
4. They grum-ble at the preach-er, they grum-ble at his prayer,
5. If you don't quit your grum-bling and stop it now and here,

Who spend their lives in grum-bling at ev-'ry-thing a-round;
They grum-ble at their neigh-bors, they think it is no harm;
And if the crops are fail-ing, they grum-ble and they sigh.
They grum-ble at his preach-ing, they grum-ble ev-'ry-where;
You'll nev-er get to heav-en, no grum-blers en-ter there.

O yes, they al-ways grum-ble, no mat-ter what we say,
They grum-ble at their hus-bands, they grum-ble at their wives,
They grum-ble at low pric-es and grum-ble when they're high,
They grum-ble at God's peo-ple and say 'tis all dis play;
Re-pent and be con-vert-ed, be saved from all your sin;

For these are chron-ic grum-blers and they grum-ble night and day.
They grum-ble at their chil-dren; but the grum-bler nev-er thrives.
They grum-ble all the year'round and they grum-ble till they die.
But ho-ly folks don't grum-ble, they have on-ly time to pray.
You know that grum-bling Christ-ians find it hard a crown to win.

CHORUS

O they grum-ble on Mon-day Tues-day, Wednes-day, grum-ble

Grum, grum, grum, grum,

GRUMBLERS

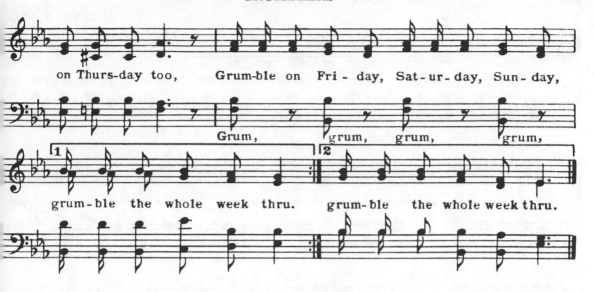

on Thurs-day too, Grum-ble on Fri - day, Sat - ur - day, Sun - day,

Grum, grum, grum, grum,

1 grum-ble the whole week thru. **2** grum-ble the whole week thru.

---

21 A SUNDAY-GO-TO-MEETIN' CHRISTIAN

H. D. L.

HARRY DIXON LOES

I want to be more than a Sun-day-go-to-meet-in' Christ-ian,(O yes!)

I want a re - li - gion that thrills me ev-'ry day;(O yes!)

Say-in' "A-men" to the preach-er is fine, If all the week I let my light shine;

I want to be more than a Sun-day-go-to-meet-in' Christ-ian.

MY LORD KNOWS THE WAY

S. E. C.

SIDNEY E. COX

My Lord knows the way thro' the wil-der-ness, all I have to do is fol-low. My

Lord knows the way thro' the wil-der-ness, all I have to do is fol-low.

Strength for to-day is mine all the way, and all I need for to-mor-row. My

Lord knows the way thro' the wil-der-ness, all I have to do is fol-low.

23 I'M GLAD I'M A BORN AGAIN CHRISTIAN

S. E. C.

SIDNEY E. COX

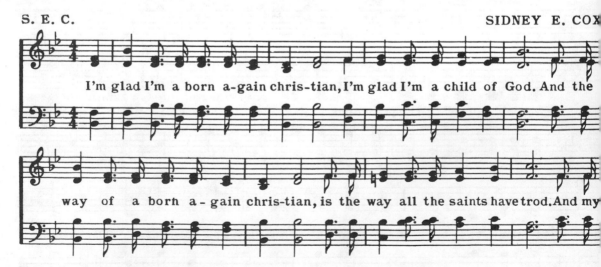

I'm glad I'm a born a-gain chris-tian, I'm glad I'm a child of God. And the

way of a born a-gain chris-tian, is the way all the saints have trod. And my

I'M GLAD I'M A BORN AGAIN CHRISTIAN

heart is sing-ing of the Sav iour's grace, and we shall all be like Him when we

see His face. I'm glad I'm a born a-gain chris-tian, I'm glad I'm a child of God.

24 GOD CAN DO ANYTHING BUT FAIL

I. F. S.

IRA STANPHILL
Arr. by Al Smith

God can do an - y-thing, an - y-thing, an - y-thing, God can
He can save, He can keep, He can cleanse, and He will, God can

do an - y-thing but fail.
do an - y-thing but fail.

He's the Al - pha and O - me - ga, the be -

gin-ing and the end, He's the fair-est of ten-thousand to my soul; God can

do an - y-thing, an - y-thing, an-y-thing, God can do an-y-thing but fail.

ON YOUR MARK, GET SET

VIRGIL P. BROCK

BLANCHE KERR BROCK

On your mark, get set, run the race of life; There's a prize a-wait-ing you; Lay a-side ev-'ry weight, each be-set-ting sin, keep the heav'n-ly goal in view. Wit-ness-es all a-round Watch-ing as you run, Nev-er fal-ter, nev-er fail; On your mark, get set, run the race of life; There's a prize a-wait-ing you.

26

HAVE FAITH IN GOD

A. M. M.

AUDREY M. MIEIR

Have Faith in God, Have Faith in God,

HAVE FAITH IN GOD

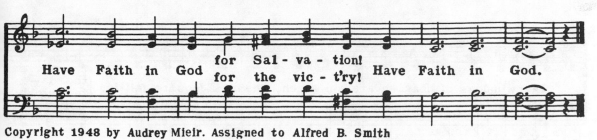

Have Faith in God for Sal-va-tion! for the vic-t'ry! Have Faith in God.

27   I KNOW WHO HOLDS THE FUTURE

A. B. S.   AL SMITH

I know who holds the fu-ture and I know He holds my hand

With God things don't just hap-pen ev-'ry-thing by Him is planned.

So as I face to-mor-row with its prob-lems large and small

I'll trust the God of mir-a-cles Give to Him my all!

THE WINDOWS OF HEAVEN

Arr. by Warren Zorn

The win-dows of Heav-en are o - pen, The bless-ings are fall-ing {to - day; / to - night;

There's joy, joy, joy in my heart, For Je - sus {has come in to stay; / makes ev-'ry-thing right; I

gave up my old tat-tered gar-ments, He gave me a robe of pure white; I'm

feast-ing on man-na from heav-en, and {Je-sus makes ev-'ry-thing right. / that's why I'm hap-py to - night.

JESUS IS OUR CAPTAIN

A.H.   ADDISON HORN

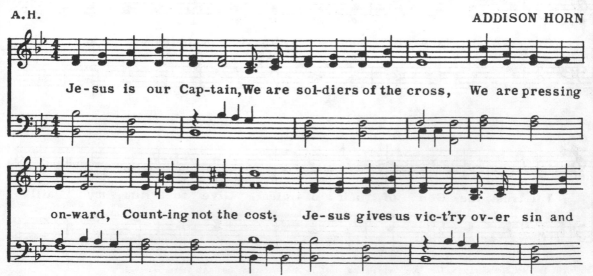

Je-sus is our Cap-tain, We are sol-diers of the cross, We are pressing

on-ward, Count-ing not the cost, Je-sus gives us vic-t'ry ov-er sin and

JESUS IS OUR CAPTAIN

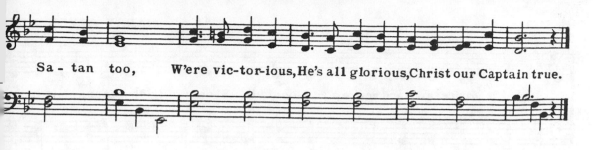

Sa - tan too, We're vic-tor-ious, He's all glorious, Christ our Captain true.

RUNNING OVER

SETH SYKES

W. GARDNER HUNTER

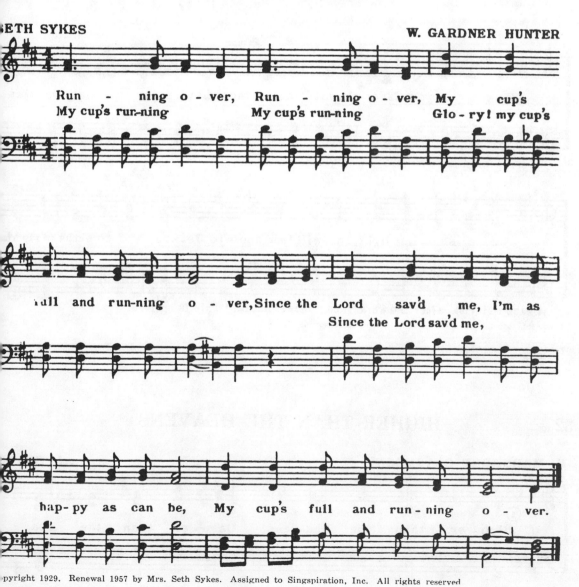

Run - ning o - ver, Run - ning o - ver, My cup's
My cup's run-ning My cup's run-ning Glo - ry! my cup's

full and run-ning o - ver, Since the Lord sav'd me, I'm as
Since the Lord sav'd me,

hap-py as can be, My cup's full and run - ning o - ver.

SHOW IT IN YOUR FACE

H. D. L.

HARRY DIXON LOES

If you're saved and you're glad a-bout it, Show it in your face, show it in your face, show it in your face; If you're saved and you're glad a-bout it, Show it in your face, show it in your face! Let the joy of sal-va-tion be a shin-ing light, That will lead souls to Je-sus, and to paths of right.

* At each asterisk, after the word "face," shout "Smile!" This is optional

HIGHER THAN THE HEAVENS

E. MARGARET CLARKSON

AL SMITH

High - er than the Hea-vens, Deep - er than the sea,

HIGHER THAN THE HEAVENS

Wi - der than the wide, wide world, is God's love for me.

① Point up ② point down ③ arms apart ④ point up ⑤ point to self.

FOR ME, FOR ME

Arr. by A. B.S.

For me, for me, for me, for me, There's a man-sion there for me; Up in that land so bright and grand, With a vic-tor's palm I'll take my stand. Oh, come with me, _____ for I'm go-ing to heav'n, you see; _____ If an-y-bod-y's gon-na be hap-py up there, It's me, me, me, me, me!

A SONG OF PRAISE

JOHN W. PETERSON

1. Man-y birds are sing-ing, "Praise Him, praise Him;" Hap-py bells are
2. We will join our voic-es Sing-ing, sing-ing, As the earth re-

ring-ing, "Praise our God."__ All the lit-tle flow-ers say,
joic-es In her Lord.__ Glad-ly now our hymns we raise,

"We will praise Him ev-'ry day; Chil-dren, join our cho-rus, Praise our God."__
Loud re-sound our songs of praise, As we join the cho-rus, Prais-ing God.__

35   GRATEFUL PRAISE

W. WALSHAM HOWE   JOHN W. PETERSON

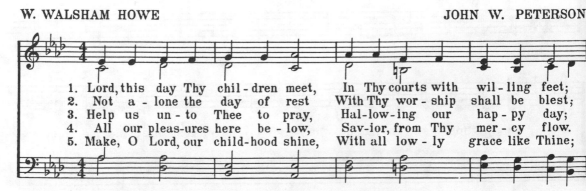

1. Lord, this day Thy chil-dren meet, In Thy courts with wil-ling feet;
2. Not a-lone the day of rest With Thy wor-ship shall be blest;
3. Help us un-to Thee to pray, Hal-low-ing our hap-py day;
4. All our pleas-ures here be-low, Sav-ior, from Thy mer-cy flow.
5. Make, O Lord, our child-hood shine, With all low-ly grace like Thine;

GRATEFUL PRAISE

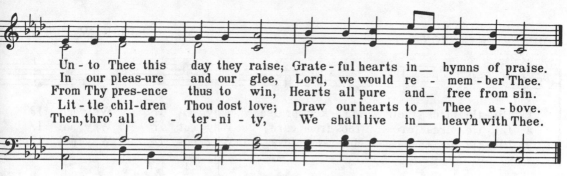

Un - to Thee this day they raise; Grate - ful hearts in __ hymns of praise.
In our pleas-ure and our glee, Lord, we would re - mem - ber Thee.
From Thy pres-ence thus to win, Hearts all pure and __ free from sin.
Lit - tle chil-dren Thou dost love; Draw our hearts to __ Thee a - bove.
Then, thro' all e - ter - ni - ty, We shall live in __ heav'n with Thee.

36

WE ARE LITTLE CHILDREN

GRACE I. FRANCES

HUBERT P. MAIN Alt.

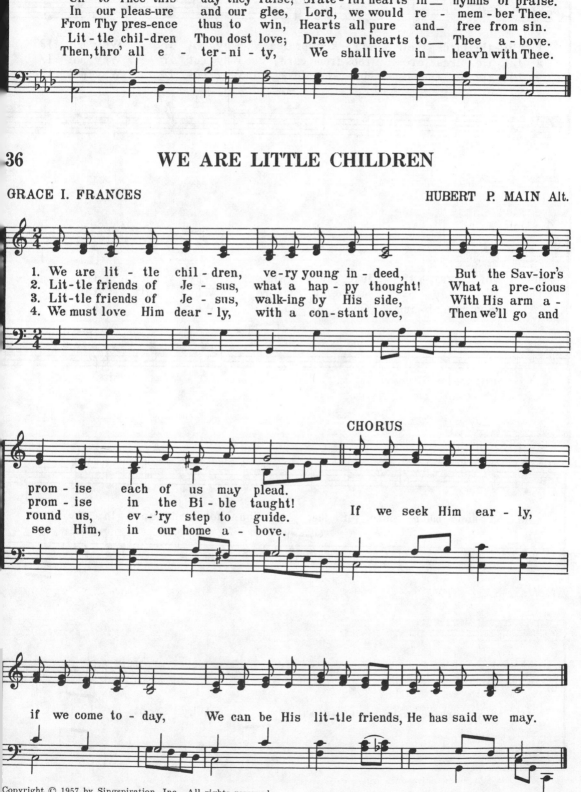

1. We are lit - tle chil - dren, ve-ry young in - deed, But the Sav-ior's
2. Lit-tle friends of Je - sus, what a hap - py thought! What a pre-cious
3. Lit-tle friends of Je - sus, walk-ing by His side, With His arm a -
4. We must love Him dear - ly, with a con-stant love, Then we'll go and

CHORUS

prom - ise each of us may plead.
prom - ise in the Bi - ble taught! If we seek Him ear - ly,
round us, ev - 'ry step to guide.
see Him, in our home a - bove.

if we come to - day, We can be His lit-tle friends, He has said we may.

WHY NOT I?

S. V. R. FORD &
JOHN W. PETERSON

JOHN W. PETERSON

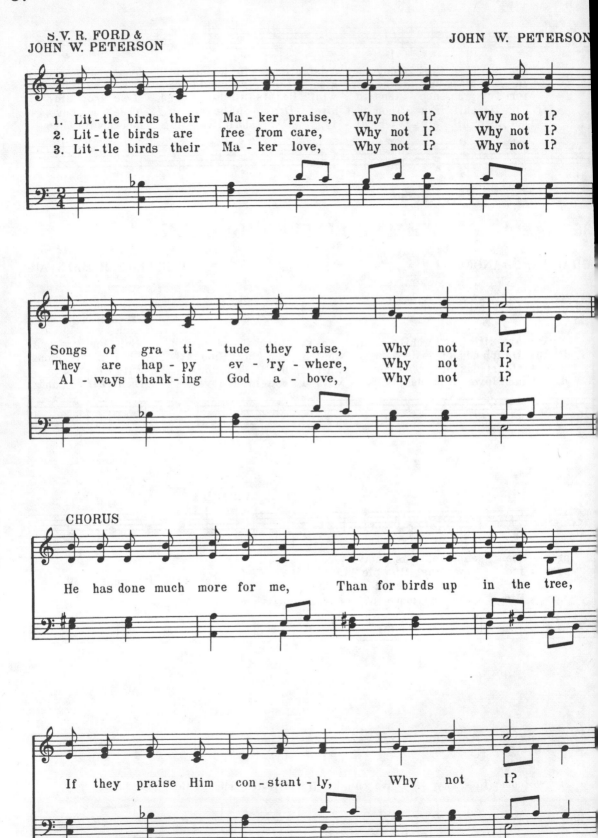

1. Lit-tle birds their Ma-ker praise, Why not I? Why not I?
2. Lit-tle birds are free from care, Why not I? Why not I?
3. Lit-tle birds their Ma-ker love, Why not I? Why not I?

Songs of gra-ti-tude they raise, Why not I?
They are hap-py ev-'ry-where, Why not I?
Al-ways thank-ing God a-bove, Why not I?

CHORUS

He has done much more for me, Than for birds up in the tree,

If they praise Him con-stant-ly, Why not I?

GOD'S CLOCK

E. MARGARET CLARKSON

HARRY DIXON LOES

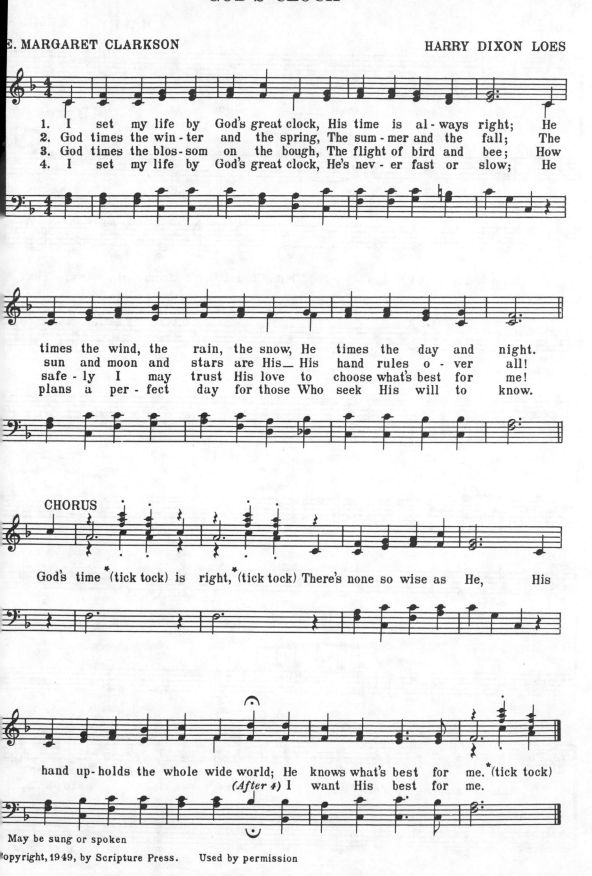

1. I set my life by God's great clock, His time is al - ways right; He
2. God times the win - ter and the spring, The sum - mer and the fall; The
3. God times the blos - som on the bough, The flight of bird and bee; How
4. I set my life by God's great clock, He's nev - er fast or slow; He

times the wind, the rain, the snow, He times the day and night.
sun and moon and stars are His_ His hand rules o - ver all!
safe - ly I may trust His love to choose what's best for me!
plans a per - fect day for those Who seek His will to know.

CHORUS

God's time *(tick tock) is right, *(tick tock) There's none so wise as He, His

hand up - holds the whole wide world; He knows what's best for me. *(tick tock)
(After 4) I want His best for me.

May be sung or spoken

GOD IS LOVE

H. D. C.

HARRY D. CLARKE

God is love ___ God is love ___

Won - der - ful sto - ry That Christ bro't from glo - ry, That

God is love ___ God is love, ___

God is love ___ Join in the cho - rus, with

this ban - ner o'er us, God is love. ___

WHICH WAY ARE YOU TRAVELING?

JOHN W. PETERSON   ALFRED B. SMITH

1. There are two ways built for lit - tle feet,
2. O 'tis sweet to know that day by day

That's the Bi - ble sto - ry; The broad way is with
Je - sus walks be - side me; With my hand in His I

dan - ger filled, The straight one leads to glo - ry.
can - not stray, And safe - ly He will guide me.

CHORUS

Which way are you trav-'ling, (trav-'ling) Which way are you trav-'ling, (trav-'ling)

Which way are you trav-'ling, The broad or nar - row way?

WHY SHOULD I CARE IF THE SUN DOESN'T SHINE?

P. K.

PHIL KERR

GIRLS: Why should I care if the sun does-n't shine? BOYS: Je-sus is mine,
all of the time. GIRLS: Why should I care if the storm clouds are low?
BOYS: Je-sus is with me I know. UNISON: He will nev-er for-sake DUET: me, ____ I am
un-der His wing. ____ Tho' tri-als o'er-take me, ____ I will praise Him and
sing. I am ev-er so hap-py So why should I care if the
sun does-n't shine? Je-sus is mine all the time. ____